THIS BOOK BELONGS TO:

And That's the Deal

For all my kids and their kids.
Especially Mia.

ethos
collective

Printed in the United States of America

Published by Ethos Collective™
PO Box 43, Powell, OH 43065
www.ethoscollective.vip

LCCN: 2021913101
Paperback ISBN: 978-1-63680-050-9   Hardcover ISBN: 978-1-63680-051-6   e-book ISBN: 978-1-63680-052-3
Available in paperback, hardcover, and e-book

AND THAT'S THE DEAL

WRITTEN BY KELLY STRYKER JOSEPH

ILLUSTRATED BY MORGAN STARKIE BLANCHARD

Which shirt would you like to wear?

I want to wear the tiger shirt.

— Sure.

What color hair tie would you like to wear?

I want the purple hair tie.

— Sure.

Which chair would you like to sit in?

I want to sit in this chair.

— Sure.

I don't want to share my toys!

But if you share your toys, your friends will enjoy playing with you. So we're going to share your toys.

.... And that's the deal.

I don't want to go
to the potty right now!

But I can tell you need
to; and when you do,
you'll be able to
concentrate more
on playing and your
tummy will feel better.
So you're going to
the potty now.

.... And that's the deal.

Do you need help
with your pants?

No, I do it.

— Sure.

I don't want to wear a hat!

But if you wear a hat, your head won't get cold
and you'll be able to stay outside longer.
So you're going to wear a hat.

.... And that's the deal.

Would you also like
to wear this scarf?

No, just the hat.

— Sure.

Which book would you like to take in the car?

The ABC book.

— Sure.

I don't want to clean up my toys!

But if you clean up your toys, we won't lose any pieces or step on them and break them. So you're going to clean up your toys.

.... And that's the deal.

Dear God,
thank you for such a wonderful day.
Help us to have another
great day tomorrow.
Amen.

Oh, Honey, I'm so tired and I don't want to sing a song too.

But, Mommy, if you sing me a song,
I'll fall asleep faster.

— Sure.

I don't want it to end!

Author Kelly Joseph would love to know what you and the children you've shared her book with have to say about it

And That's the Deal.

Visit

KikiBooksLLC.com

to share your feedback today!

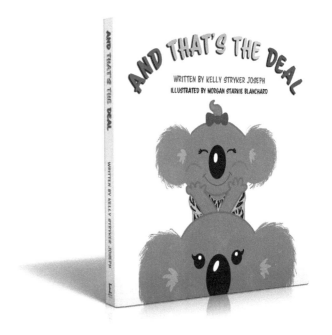